Set Free Journal

SPIRITUAL FORMATION & REFLECTION

TARYN NERGAARD

www.tarynnergaard.com

Edited by Jennie G. Scott.

Cover & interior design by Typewriter Creative Co. Cover illustration by Marsala Digital 2 on CreativeMarket.com.

ISBN 978-1-7770331-0-1

*To those who strain to grow
towards the light.*

Contents

Introduction

Hi, friend.

I wish I could tell you that I created this journal just for you, but truthfully, I created it for myself first.

I've known for several years that the closeness I feel with God often corresponds to how much time I spend with him. More than that, it depends on my daily conversations with him—the active listening, the childlike questions, the adult doubts, and the humble posture.

I also know that I experience the most growth when I bring those conversations to life by applying what he has spoken to me and moving forward how he has directed me.

But somehow life creeps in and what felt important yesterday gets pushed aside by what feels urgent now. Maybe you can relate to how suddenly a day goes by and then a week and maybe even a month or more since you last had a good heart-to-heart with God. Then that closeness you once felt has slipped away and the ache of spiritual growth has changed to the pain of spiritual stagnation.

Those are the feelings I experienced recently and the reason I created this journal. I wanted to get back to a daily habit of abiding deeply in Christ.

This journal you hold in your hands is neither a promise nor a commandment. It holds no power to change your life. What it does contain is an invitation. It's an invitation to meet daily with God and to reflect weekly on how you're doing now and where you can continue to grow.

So, if you need more of Jesus—if your soul craves to be more surrendered to the life God is calling you to, then I hope this journal gently, but firmly, takes you by the hand and draws you nearer and deeper into the hope, joy, peace, and purpose that Jesus promises.

I'm with you.

- Taryn

Using the Journal

On the following pages you'll find recommendations for how I see this journal being used. I call these recommendations rather than instructions because I trust that God will lead you through your daily time with him. However, I believe this section to be important so I know that I'm helping you make the most out of this little journal and your investment in your spiritual formation.

In addition to this "Using the Journal" section, be sure to flip to the back of the journal to the "Resources" section as I've provided reading plans, prayers, lists of emotions, and more.

WHAT I LEARNED

This one-page prompt is to remind you to keep track of what stands out to you over the next three months. Too often we let months and years slip by before we reflect on what we've learned and who we've become because of those lessons. So let's make this an important first step right up front.

Whenever you feel something stand out to you that feels meaningful—whether it's silly or sacred[1]—jot it down so you remember.

DAILY BIBLE READING

According to a study done by LifeWay research in 2017, almost nine out of ten American households own a Bible but more than half of Americans have read little or none of the Bible.[2]

> "Overall, Americans seem to like the Bible but don't have much urgency about reading it." - Scott McConnell, executive director of LifeWay Research

If you fit into the 53% of people who have read less than half of the Bible, you likely haven't experienced the Bible as an intimate, active conversation with God.

If you have read through the Bible in the past but struggle to make it a meaningful part of your day, it's time to view the Bible as a method of life transformation through communication with God.

Information + Application = Transformation

Studying your Bible is important. It's good to know the context in which words are said and understand the meaning behind specific words and verses. But if the purpose of reading your Bible is to analyze the text without learning how to apply it to your life, then you're missing out on the opportunity for transformational life change.

Most of us don't plan on becoming theologians and biblical scholars, so why do we spend our reading time acting like knowledge is the ultimate goal?

When we begin a conversation with God through His Word, we gain a better understanding of our purpose, our direction, and our immediate next steps. He gives us the wisdom we need to honor him with our lives.

What You Need

To read God's word, you need a Bible. For this method, I recommend a physical Bible, but the YouVersion Bible app is a good second choice. Be sure to choose a translation you can understand.

Additionally, have this journal and a pen ready.

What to Read

Pick a book of the Bible and read through it in small portions each day (10-15 verses). It's better to read a small passage that you can remember and apply to your life than a large passage that overwhelms you with information.

Tip: If you're new to reading the Bible, start in the New Testament.

Write it Down

When we want to remember something important, we write it down. We should do the same thing when we spend time with God. Expect him to speak to you and value his words enough to remember them.

On your daily journal pages, write the date and reflect on how you are feeling at the moment. Be as specific as possible. If recognizing your emotions is difficult or new for you, see the resource section for help.

Next, follow the format as you go through the steps.

- Read
- Receive (no journal space for this prompt)
- Reflect
- Respond
- Remember

Read

Start reading. When something stands out to you, use your pen to place a mark in your Bible. Marking with a pen gives you more options than simply highlighting everything.

I use a small tick (`) to note something that stood out to me. For parts that really catch my attention, I use square brackets ([ ]) around the phrase. For single words that seem significant or are repeated, I use an underline (_).

Choose what works best for you. The purpose is to engage with what you are reading.

In your journal, write down the verse you read. You can also include a summary in your own words.

Receive

After you've written down the part of the passage that stood out to you, pray. Ask God what message or truth he wants to impress upon you with that Scripture.

Dig deeper by asking specific questions:

What do you want to teach me with this verse? How does this verse apply to my day today? Is there something you would like me to start doing? Is there something you would like me to stop doing?

Through this process, you are engaging in conversation with God regarding what he wants to talk to you about.

Reflect

Now take the time to write down what you feel God spoke to you. You don't need to worry about getting it exactly right! Just summarize the general message you felt he was trying to impress upon you.

If any other Bible verses come to your mind that relate to what you read, write them down in the margin to look up later.

In addition, take a moment to think of any action steps you can apply to your day or your life based on what you've just learned.

Respond

Now is the time to continue the conversation with God through prayer. Thank God for his faithfulness in your life, the truths he is teaching you, or anything else for which you feel grateful.

It's at this point in my own routine that I bring my wants, needs, and desires before God. By focusing on learning from him first and then bringing my needs to him second, I come before him with humility and openness.

Write your prayers in your journal as a way to recall past requests and remind yourself of his faithfulness.

Remember

Write out a verse to memorize this week. Writing it out will help you to remember it, and being able to recall Scripture is an important part of connecting your daily life to God's presence.

If you find Scripture memorization challenging, don't put pressure on yourself to memorize a new verse each week. Simply repeat the same verse until you're ready to move on.

The Holy Spirit

When Christ ascended to heaven, he promised his disciples that he would send them a helper. We understand this helper to be the Holy Spirit--an integral, but often overlooked, part of the Trinity.

When we engage in a conversation with God through the Holy Spirit, we are able to hear his Word speaking directly into our lives.

One of the greatest transformations of my life came as I learned to engage in my daily Bible reading this way.[2]

WEEKLY REFLECTION

This is an opportunity to recognize what is going well and where you need to make adjustments. Rather than allowing certain emotions or relational conflicts to build up, you can address them more frequently.

Personal Reflection

Be honest and allow yourself to celebrate the highs and make space for the lows. We cannot grow from a place of shame, so it's best to "make friends" with all the parts of ourselves, even the ones we'd like to change.

Relational Reflection

If you're not used to dealing with conflict or you live in a constant state of shame or bitterness, this section might feel unbearable at first. But take heart—as we learn to make this a regular part of our lives, it becomes a practice that changes us from the inside out. It is worth the discomfort.

First, think of any hurts you feel from this week (or if some of them have lingered there longer, address these too). When our hurt is left unaddressed, it becomes bitterness—a self-inflicted poison of our souls.

Use the Prayer of Forgiveness in the Resources section or pray your own prayer of forgiveness to release the hurt and bitterness. Even if you think something *isn't a big deal*, it's best to forgive the person now. Relational molehills do become mountains when we ignore them too long.

Next, identify anyone you may have hurt this week. Use the Prayer of Repentance to admit your wrongdoing to God, then make things right with the person you hurt (see Resource section for helpful information).

We live in a lonely culture, yet we're often waiting for others to go first in initiating friendships. Make the decision to connect with someone in person or through a phone call or text each week.

Spiritual Reflection

This section of your weekly reflection helps pull together your daily time with God. Look back through your "Reflect" writing from each day and identify any similar impressions you felt God spoke to you.

Has God been affirming similar ideas or truths to you through other sources? This is the place to make those connections and recognize all the ways God is speaking to you regularly.

After your week of spending daily time with God, are there any questions you have for him? Don't be afraid to search your heart and mind for areas of doubt you are facing. God can handle our questions and doubts—it does not mean we lack faith!

Coming before God with an open and honest heart is what he desires.

Next Week

It's important to have something to look forward to. It can be anything of any size—as long as it brings you joy! If you can't think of anything you are looking forward to, plan something now.

Additionally, this is your space to decide a verse to memorize next week. Again, don't push yourself to move on to a new verse if you're still learning the one from this week. Keep going with the same one until you're comfortable with it. This isn't a race or a competition, so go as slow and steady as you need.

See a sample of the journal on the following pages.

Date: January 1, 2020

Today, I feel isolated and disappointed.

READ

Today, I read Philippians 1:1-14

What stood out to me is:

Verse 6 "he who began a good work in you will carry it

out to completion..."

REFLECT

What I best sense God speaking to me is:

He is faithful. I don't need to know all the answers or

see what's coming in the future—I can trust that God is

working out the details. Have faith!

The one thing I will surrender to God today is:

Whether or not I get the job. If I'm supposed to have

the position, you'll work it out. If not, I'll be okay. I was

faithful in applying.

One next step I can take today is:

Plan my budget for this month.

RESPOND

God, thank you for reminding me not to worry because you're in control. Help me trust you when I'm feeling overwhelmed and anxious. Please show what is important to focus on today and help me let go of everything else. Be with me today as I parent and work—give me patience and love for everyone I'm around today. Thank you God. Amen.

REMEMBER

Romans 8:5-6

For those who live according to the flesh have their minds set on the things of the flesh, but those who live according to the Spirit have their minds set on the things of the Spirit. Now the mind-set of the flesh is death, but the mind-set of the Spirit is life and peace.

Weekly Reflection

PERSONAL REFLECTION

What went well this week?
We had a relaxing time over the holidays as a family. I
didn't get anxious about things that weren't important.

Three things I am grateful for are:
1. Our little family
2. Meaningful work
3. Our church

What feeling(s) did I experience most frequently? Why?
Isolated, lonely. The holidays remind me that people
around me don't know me very well. It would be nice to
feel truly seen and known.

What thoughts or worries have come to mind most frequently?
That I may never really fit in or be included.

RELATIONAL REFLECTION

Who do I need to forgive?
Jessica

With whom do I need to make things right?

Becca

I will do that by:

Apologizing for not texting her over the holidays and

inviting her for coffee.

One person I will connect with next week is:

Becca

SPIRITUAL REFLECTION

Is there a theme God has been speaking to me about this week
through Bible reading, worship, books, or sermons?

That everyone feels rejection. I should still choose

to connect with people and not feel hurt when

relationships aren't reciprocated.

The questions I have for God right now are:

Why are relationships so hard?? How can I be a better

wife and a better friend?

NEXT WEEK

What am I looking forward to?

My kid-free day!

Next week's memory verse:

Romans 8:37-39

Journal

What I Learned

1.

2.

3.

4.

5.

6.

7.

8.

9.

10.

Week of:

....

For freedom, Christ set us free. Stand firm then and don't submit again to a yoke of slavery.

Galatians 5:1

Date: ....

Today, I feel ....

READ

Today, I read ....

What stood out to me is:

....

....

REFLECT

What I best sense God speaking to me is:

....

....

....

The one thing I will surrender to God today is:

....

....

....

One next step I can take today is:

....

....

RESPOND

REMEMBER

Date: ....

Today, I feel ....

READ

Today, I read ....

What stood out to me is:

....

....

REFLECT

What I best sense God speaking to me is:

....

....

....

The one thing I will surrender to God today is:

....

....

....

One next step I can take today is:

....

....

RESPOND

REMEMBER

Date:

Today, I feel ....

READ

Today, I read ....

What stood out to me is:

....

....

REFLECT

What I best sense God speaking to me is:

....

....

....

The one thing I will surrender to God today is:

....

....

....

One next step I can take today is:

....

....

RESPOND

REMEMBER

Date:

Today, I feel ....

READ

Today, I read ....

What stood out to me is:

....

....

REFLECT

What I best sense God speaking to me is:

....

....

....

The one thing I will surrender to God today is:

....

....

....

One next step I can take today is:

....

....

RESPOND

REMEMBER

Date:

Today, I feel ....

READ

Today, I read ....

What stood out to me is:

....

....

REFLECT

What I best sense God speaking to me is:

....

....

....

The one thing I will surrender to God today is:

....

....

....

One next step I can take today is:

....

....

RESPOND

REMEMBER

Weekly Reflection

PERSONAL REFLECTION

What went well this week?

....

....

Three things I am grateful for are:

1. ....

2. ....

3. ....

What feeling(s) did I experience most frequently? Why?

....

....

....

What thoughts or worries have come to mind most frequently?

....

....

RELATIONAL REFLECTION

Who do I need to forgive?

....

With whom do I need to make things right?

....

I will do that by:

....

....

One person I will connect with next week is:

....

SPIRITUAL REFLECTION

Is there a theme God has been speaking to me about this week through Bible reading, worship, books, or sermons?

....

....

....

The questions I have for God right now are:

....

....

....

NEXT WEEK

What am I looking forward to?

....

Next week's memory verse:

....

Week of:

....

I called to the Lord in distress; the Lord answered me and put me in a spacious place.

Psalm 118:5

Date:

Today, I feel ....

READ

Today, I read ....

What stood out to me is:

....

....

REFLECT

What I best sense God speaking to me is:

....

....

....

The one thing I will surrender to God today is:

....

....

....

One next step I can take today is:

....

....

RESPOND

REMEMBER

Date:

Today, I feel ....

READ

Today, I read ....

What stood out to me is:

....

....

REFLECT

What I best sense God speaking to me is:

....

....

....

The one thing I will surrender to God today is:

....

....

....

One next step I can take today is:

....

....

RESPOND

REMEMBER

Date:
....

Today, I feel ....

READ

Today, I read ....

What stood out to me is:

....

....

REFLECT

What I best sense God speaking to me is:

....

....

....

The one thing I will surrender to God today is:

....

....

....

One next step I can take today is:

....

....

RESPOND

REMEMBER

Date: ....

Today, I feel ....

READ

Today, I read ....

What stood out to me is:

....

....

REFLECT

What I best sense God speaking to me is:

....

....

....

The one thing I will surrender to God today is:

....

....

....

One next step I can take today is:

....

....

RESPOND

REMEMBER

Date: ....

Today, I feel ....

READ

Today, I read ....

What stood out to me is:

....

....

REFLECT

What I best sense God speaking to me is:

....

....

....

The one thing I will surrender to God today is:

....

....

....

One next step I can take today is:

....

....

RESPOND

REMEMBER

Weekly Reflection

PERSONAL REFLECTION

What went well this week?

....

....

Three things I am grateful for are:

1. ....

2. ....

3. ....

What feeling(s) did I experience most frequently? Why?

....

....

....

What thoughts or worries have come to mind most frequently?

....

....

RELATIONAL REFLECTION

Who do I need to forgive?

....

With whom do I need to make things right?

....

I will do that by:

....

....

One person I will connect with next week is:

....

SPIRITUAL REFLECTION

Is there a theme God has been speaking to me about this week
through Bible reading, worship, books, or sermons?

....

....

....

The questions I have for God right now are:

....

....

....

NEXT WEEK

What am I looking forward to?

....

Next week's memory verse:

....

Week of:

....

Jesus spoke to them again: "I am the light of the world. Anyone who follows me will never walk in the darkness but will have the light of life."

John 8:12

Date: ....

Today, I feel ....

READ

Today, I read ....

What stood out to me is:

....

....

REFLECT

What I best sense God speaking to me is:

....

....

....

The one thing I will surrender to God today is:

....

....

....

One next step I can take today is:

....

....

RESPOND

REMEMBER

Date:

Today, I feel ....

READ

Today, I read ....

What stood out to me is:

....

....

REFLECT

What I best sense God speaking to me is:

....

....

....

The one thing I will surrender to God today is:

....

....

....

One next step I can take today is:

....

....

RESPOND

REMEMBER

Date:

Today, I feel ....

READ

Today, I read ....

What stood out to me is:

....

....

REFLECT

What I best sense God speaking to me is:

....

....

....

The one thing I will surrender to God today is:

....

....

....

One next step I can take today is:

....

....

RESPOND

REMEMBER

Date:

Today, I feel ....

READ

Today, I read ....

What stood out to me is:

....

....

REFLECT

What I best sense God speaking to me is:

....

....

....

The one thing I will surrender to God today is:

....

....

....

One next step I can take today is:

....

....

RESPOND

REMEMBER

61

Date: ....

Today, I feel ....

READ

Today, I read ....

What stood out to me is:

....

....

REFLECT

What I best sense God speaking to me is:

....

....

....

The one thing I will surrender to God today is:

....

....

....

One next step I can take today is:

....

....

RESPOND

REMEMBER

Weekly Reflection

PERSONAL REFLECTION

What went well this week?

....

....

Three things I am grateful for are:

1. ....

2. ....

3. ....

What feeling(s) did I experience most frequently? Why?

....

....

....

What thoughts or worries have come to mind most frequently?

....

....

RELATIONAL REFLECTION

Who do I need to forgive?

....

With whom do I need to make things right?

....

I will do that by:

....

....

One person I will connect with next week is:

....

SPIRITUAL REFLECTION

Is there a theme God has been speaking to me about this week through Bible reading, worship, books, or sermons?

....

....

....

The questions I have for God right now are:

....

....

....

NEXT WEEK

What am I looking forward to?

....

Next week's memory verse:

....

Week of:

....

Now the Lord is the Spirit, and where the Spirit of the Lord is, there is freedom.

2 Corinthians 3:17

Date: ....

Today, I feel ....

READ

Today, I read ....

What stood out to me is:

....

....

REFLECT

What I best sense God speaking to me is:

....

....

....

The one thing I will surrender to God today is:

....

....

....

One next step I can take today is:

....

....

RESPOND

REMEMBER

Date: ....

Today, I feel ....

READ

Today, I read ....

What stood out to me is:

....

....

REFLECT

What I best sense God speaking to me is:

....

....

....

The one thing I will surrender to God today is:

....

....

....

One next step I can take today is:

....

....

RESPOND

REMEMBER

Date:

Today, I feel ....

READ

Today, I read ....

What stood out to me is:

....

....

REFLECT

What I best sense God speaking to me is:

....

....

....

The one thing I will surrender to God today is:

....

....

....

One next step I can take today is:

....

....

RESPOND

REMEMBER

Date:

Today, I feel ....

READ

Today, I read ....

What stood out to me is:

....

....

REFLECT

What I best sense God speaking to me is:

....

....

....

The one thing I will surrender to God today is:

....

....

....

One next step I can take today is:

....

....

RESPOND

REMEMBER

Date:

Today, I feel ....

READ

Today, I read ....

What stood out to me is:

....

....

REFLECT

What I best sense God speaking to me is:

....

....

....

The one thing I will surrender to God today is:

....

....

....

One next step I can take today is:

....

....

RESPOND

REMEMBER

Weekly Reflection

PERSONAL REFLECTION

What went well this week?

....

....

Three things I am grateful for are:

1. ....

2. ....

3. ....

What feeling(s) did I experience most frequently? Why?

....

....

....

What thoughts or worries have come to mind most frequently?

....

....

RELATIONAL REFLECTION

Who do I need to forgive?

....

With whom do I need to make things right?

....

I will do that by:

....

....

One person I will connect with next week is:

....

SPIRITUAL REFLECTION

Is there a theme God has been speaking to me about this week through Bible reading, worship, books, or sermons?

....

....

....

The questions I have for God right now are:

....

....

....

NEXT WEEK

What am I looking forward to?

....

Next week's memory verse:

....

Week of:

....

This is my comfort in my affliction: Your promise
has given me life.

Psalm 119:50

Date: ....

Today, I feel ....

READ

Today, I read ....

What stood out to me is:

....

....

REFLECT

What I best sense God speaking to me is:

....

....

....

The one thing I will surrender to God today is:

....

....

....

One next step I can take today is:

....

....

RESPOND

REMEMBER

Date: ....

Today, I feel ....

READ

Today, I read ....

What stood out to me is:

....

....

REFLECT

What I best sense God speaking to me is:

....

....

....

The one thing I will surrender to God today is:

....

....

....

One next step I can take today is:

....

....

RESPOND

REMEMBER

Date:

Today, I feel ....

READ

Today, I read ....

What stood out to me is:

....

....

REFLECT

What I best sense God speaking to me is:

....

....

....

The one thing I will surrender to God today is:

....

....

....

One next step I can take today is:

....

....

RESPOND

REMEMBER

Date: ....

Today, I feel ....

READ

Today, I read ....

What stood out to me is:

....

....

REFLECT

What I best sense God speaking to me is:

....

....

....

The one thing I will surrender to God today is:

....

....

....

One next step I can take today is:

....

....

RESPOND

REMEMBER

Date:

Today, I feel ....

READ

Today, I read ....

What stood out to me is:

....

....

REFLECT

What I best sense God speaking to me is:

....

....

....

The one thing I will surrender to God today is:

....

....

....

One next step I can take today is:

....

....

RESPOND

REMEMBER

Weekly Reflection

PERSONAL REFLECTION

What went well this week?

....

....

Three things I am grateful for are:

1. ....

2. ....

3. ....

What feeling(s) did I experience most frequently? Why?

....

....

....

What thoughts or worries have come to mind most frequently?

....

....

RELATIONAL REFLECTION

Who do I need to forgive?

....

With whom do I need to make things right?

....

I will do that by:

....

....

One person I will connect with next week is:

....

SPIRITUAL REFLECTION

Is there a theme God has been speaking to me about this week through Bible reading, worship, books, or sermons?

....

....

....

The questions I have for God right now are:

....

....

....

NEXT WEEK

What am I looking forward to?

....

Next week's memory verse:

....

Week of:

....

For you were called to be free, brothers and sisters; only don't use this freedom as an opportunity for the flesh, but serve one another through love.

Galatians 5:13

Date:

Today, I feel ....

READ

Today, I read ....

What stood out to me is:

....

....

REFLECT

What I best sense God speaking to me is:

....

....

....

The one thing I will surrender to God today is:

....

....

....

One next step I can take today is:

....

....

RESPOND

REMEMBER

Date: ....

Today, I feel ....

READ

Today, I read ....

What stood out to me is:

....

....

REFLECT

What I best sense God speaking to me is:

....

....

....

The one thing I will surrender to God today is:

....

....

....

One next step I can take today is:

....

....

RESPOND

REMEMBER

Date:

Today, I feel ....

READ

Today, I read ....

What stood out to me is:

....

....

REFLECT

What I best sense God speaking to me is:

....

....

....

The one thing I will surrender to God today is:

....

....

....

One next step I can take today is:

....

....

RESPOND

REMEMBER

Date: ....

Today, I feel ....

READ

Today, I read ....

What stood out to me is:

....

....

REFLECT

What I best sense God speaking to me is:

....

....

....

The one thing I will surrender to God today is:

....

....

....

One next step I can take today is:

....

....

RESPOND

REMEMBER

Date: ....

Today, I feel ....

READ

Today, I read ....

What stood out to me is:

....

....

REFLECT

What I best sense God speaking to me is:

....

....

....

The one thing I will surrender to God today is:

....

....

....

One next step I can take today is:

....

....

RESPOND

REMEMBER

Weekly Reflection

PERSONAL REFLECTION

What went well this week?

....

....

Three things I am grateful for are:

1. ....

2. ....

3. ....

What feeling(s) did I experience most frequently? Why?

....

....

....

What thoughts or worries have come to mind most frequently?

....

....

RELATIONAL REFLECTION

Who do I need to forgive?

....

With whom do I need to make things right?

....

I will do that by:

....

....

One person I will connect with next week is:

....

SPIRITUAL REFLECTION

Is there a theme God has been speaking to me about this week
through Bible reading, worship, books, or sermons?

....

....

....

The questions I have for God right now are:

....

....

....

NEXT WEEK

What am I looking forward to?

....

Next week's memory verse:

....

Week of:

....

But now, since you have been set free from sin and have become enslaved to God, you have your fruit, which results in sanctification—and the outcome is eternal life!

Romans 6:22

Date: ....

Today, I feel ....

READ

Today, I read ....

What stood out to me is:

....

....

REFLECT

What I best sense God speaking to me is:

....

....

....

The one thing I will surrender to God today is:

....

....

....

One next step I can take today is:

....

....

RESPOND

REMEMBER

Date:

Today, I feel

READ

Today, I read

What stood out to me is:

REFLECT

What I best sense God speaking to me is:

The one thing I will surrender to God today is:

One next step I can take today is:

RESPOND

REMEMBER

Date: ....

Today, I feel ....

READ

Today, I read ....

What stood out to me is:

....

....

REFLECT

What I best sense God speaking to me is:

....

....

....

The one thing I will surrender to God today is:

....

....

....

One next step I can take today is:

....

....

RESPOND

REMEMBER

115

Date:

Today, I feel ....

READ

Today, I read ....

What stood out to me is:

....

....

REFLECT

What I best sense God speaking to me is:

....

....

....

The one thing I will surrender to God today is:

....

....

....

One next step I can take today is:

....

....

RESPOND

REMEMBER

Date: ....

Today, I feel ....

READ

Today, I read ....

What stood out to me is:

....

....

REFLECT

What I best sense God speaking to me is:

....

....

....

The one thing I will surrender to God today is:

....

....

....

One next step I can take today is:

....

....

RESPOND

REMEMBER

119

Weekly Reflection

PERSONAL REFLECTION

What went well this week?

....

....

Three things I am grateful for are:

1. ....

2. ....

3. ....

What feeling(s) did I experience most frequently? Why?

....

....

....

What thoughts or worries have come to mind most frequently?

....

....

RELATIONAL REFLECTION

Who do I need to forgive?

....

With whom do I need to make things right?

....

I will do that by:

....

....

One person I will connect with next week is:

....

SPIRITUAL REFLECTION

Is there a theme God has been speaking to me about this week through Bible reading, worship, books, or sermons?

....

....

....

The questions I have for God right now are:

....

....

....

NEXT WEEK

What am I looking forward to?

....

Next week's memory verse:

....

Week of:

....

So if the Son sets you free, you really will be free.

John 8:36

Date:

Today, I feel ....

READ

Today, I read ....

What stood out to me is:

....

....

REFLECT

What I best sense God speaking to me is:

....

....

....

The one thing I will surrender to God today is:

....

....

....

One next step I can take today is:

....

....

RESPOND

REMEMBER

Date: ....

Today, I feel ....

READ

Today, I read ....

What stood out to me is:

....

....

REFLECT

What I best sense God speaking to me is:

....

....

....

The one thing I will surrender to God today is:

....

....

....

One next step I can take today is:

....

....

RESPOND

REMEMBER

Date:

Today, I feel ....

READ

Today, I read ....

What stood out to me is:

....

....

REFLECT

What I best sense God speaking to me is:

....

....

....

The one thing I will surrender to God today is:

....

....

....

One next step I can take today is:

....

....

RESPOND

REMEMBER

Date:

Today, I feel ....

READ

Today, I read ....

What stood out to me is:

....

....

REFLECT

What I best sense God speaking to me is:

....

....

....

The one thing I will surrender to God today is:

....

....

....

One next step I can take today is:

....

....

RESPOND

REMEMBER

Date:

Today, I feel ....

READ

Today, I read ....

What stood out to me is:

....

....

REFLECT

What I best sense God speaking to me is:

....

....

....

The one thing I will surrender to God today is:

....

....

....

One next step I can take today is:

....

....

RESPOND

REMEMBER

Weekly Reflection

PERSONAL REFLECTION

What went well this week?

....

....

Three things I am grateful for are:

1. ....

2. ....

3. ....

What feeling(s) did I experience most frequently? Why?

....

....

....

What thoughts or worries have come to mind most frequently?

....

....

RELATIONAL REFLECTION

Who do I need to forgive?

....

With whom do I need to make things right?

....

I will do that by:

....

....

One person I will connect with next week is:

....

SPIRITUAL REFLECTION

Is there a theme God has been speaking to me about this week through Bible reading, worship, books, or sermons?

....

....

....

The questions I have for God right now are:

....

....

....

NEXT WEEK

What am I looking forward to?

....

Next week's memory verse:

....

Week of:

....

For as the earth produces its growth, and as a garden enables what is sown to spring up, so the Lord God will cause righteousness and praise to spring up before all the nations.

Isaiah 61:11

Date:

Today, I feel ....

READ

Today, I read ....

What stood out to me is:

....

....

REFLECT

What I best sense God speaking to me is:

....

....

....

The one thing I will surrender to God today is:

....

....

....

One next step I can take today is:

....

....

RESPOND

REMEMBER

Date: ....

Today, I feel ....

READ

Today, I read ....

What stood out to me is:

....

....

REFLECT

What I best sense God speaking to me is:

....

....

....

The one thing I will surrender to God today is:

....

....

....

One next step I can take today is:

....

....

RESPOND

REMEMBER

Date: ....

Today, I feel ....

READ

Today, I read ....

What stood out to me is:

....

....

REFLECT

What I best sense God speaking to me is:

....

....

....

The one thing I will surrender to God today is:

....

....

....

One next step I can take today is:

....

....

RESPOND

REMEMBER

Date:

Today, I feel ....

READ

Today, I read ....

What stood out to me is:

....

....

REFLECT

What I best sense God speaking to me is:

....

....

....

The one thing I will surrender to God today is:

....

....

....

One next step I can take today is:

....

....

RESPOND

REMEMBER

Date:

Today, I feel ....

READ

Today, I read ....

What stood out to me is:

....

....

REFLECT

What I best sense God speaking to me is:

....

....

....

The one thing I will surrender to God today is:

....

....

....

One next step I can take today is:

....

....

RESPOND

REMEMBER

Weekly Reflection

PERSONAL REFLECTION

What went well this week?

....

....

Three things I am grateful for are:

1. ....

2. ....

3. ....

What feeling(s) did I experience most frequently? Why?

....

....

....

What thoughts or worries have come to mind most frequently?

....

....

RELATIONAL REFLECTION

Who do I need to forgive?

....

With whom do I need to make things right?

....

I will do that by:

....

....

One person I will connect with next week is:

....

SPIRITUAL REFLECTION

Is there a theme God has been speaking to me about this week through Bible reading, worship, books, or sermons?

....

....

....

The questions I have for God right now are:

....

....

....

NEXT WEEK

What am I looking forward to?

....

Next week's memory verse:

....

Week of:

....

Now those who belong to Christ Jesus have crucified the flesh with its passions and desires.

Galatians 5:24

Date: ....

Today, I feel ....

READ

Today, I read ....

What stood out to me is:

....

....

REFLECT

What I best sense God speaking to me is:

....

....

....

The one thing I will surrender to God today is:

....

....

....

One next step I can take today is:

....

....

RESPOND

REMEMBER

153

Date:

Today, I feel ....

READ

Today, I read ....

What stood out to me is:

....

....

REFLECT

What I best sense God speaking to me is:

....

....

....

The one thing I will surrender to God today is:

....

....

....

One next step I can take today is:

....

....

RESPOND

REMEMBER

Date:

Today, I feel ....

READ

Today, I read ....

What stood out to me is:

....

....

REFLECT

What I best sense God speaking to me is:

....

....

....

The one thing I will surrender to God today is:

....

....

....

One next step I can take today is:

....

....

RESPOND

REMEMBER

Date:

Today, I feel ....

READ

Today, I read ....

What stood out to me is:

....

....

REFLECT

What I best sense God speaking to me is:

....

....

....

The one thing I will surrender to God today is:

....

....

....

One next step I can take today is:

....

....

RESPOND

REMEMBER

Date:

Today, I feel ....

READ

Today, I read ....

What stood out to me is:

....

....

REFLECT

What I best sense God speaking to me is:

....

....

....

The one thing I will surrender to God today is:

....

....

....

One next step I can take today is:

....

....

RESPOND

REMEMBER

Weekly Reflection

PERSONAL REFLECTION

What went well this week?

....

....

Three things I am grateful for are:

1. ....

2. ....

3. ....

What feeling(s) did I experience most frequently? Why?

....

....

....

What thoughts or worries have come to mind most frequently?

....

....

RELATIONAL REFLECTION

Who do I need to forgive?

....

With whom do I need to make things right?

....

I will do that by:

....

....

One person I will connect with next week is:

....

SPIRITUAL REFLECTION

Is there a theme God has been speaking to me about this week through Bible reading, worship, books, or sermons?

....

....

....

The questions I have for God right now are:

....

....

....

NEXT WEEK

What am I looking forward to?

....

Next week's memory verse:

....

Week of:

....

"Everything is permissible for me," but not everything is beneficial. "Everything is permissible for me," but I will not be mastered by anything.

1 Corinthians 6:12

Date:

Today, I feel ....

READ

Today, I read ....

What stood out to me is:

....

....

REFLECT

What I best sense God speaking to me is:

....

....

....

The one thing I will surrender to God today is:

....

....

....

One next step I can take today is:

....

....

RESPOND

REMEMBER

Date:

Today, I feel ....

READ

Today, I read ....

What stood out to me is:

....

....

REFLECT

What I best sense God speaking to me is:

....

....

....

The one thing I will surrender to God today is:

....

....

....

One next step I can take today is:

....

....

RESPOND

REMEMBER

Date:

Today, I feel ....

READ

Today, I read ....

What stood out to me is:

....

....

REFLECT

What I best sense God speaking to me is:

....

....

....

The one thing I will surrender to God today is:

....

....

....

One next step I can take today is:

....

....

RESPOND

REMEMBER

Date: ....

Today, I feel ....

READ

Today, I read ....

What stood out to me is:

....

....

REFLECT

What I best sense God speaking to me is:

....

....

....

The one thing I will surrender to God today is:

....

....

....

One next step I can take today is:

....

....

RESPOND

REMEMBER

173

Date: ....

Today, I feel ....

READ

Today, I read ....

What stood out to me is:

....

....

REFLECT

What I best sense God speaking to me is:

....

....

....

The one thing I will surrender to God today is:

....

....

....

One next step I can take today is:

....

....

RESPOND

REMEMBER

Weekly Reflection

PERSONAL REFLECTION

What went well this week?

....

....

Three things I am grateful for are:

1. ....

2. ....

3. ....

What feeling(s) did I experience most frequently? Why?

....

....

....

What thoughts or worries have come to mind most frequently?

....

....

RELATIONAL REFLECTION

Who do I need to forgive?

....

With whom do I need to make things right?

....

I will do that by:

....

....

One person I will connect with next week is:

....

SPIRITUAL REFLECTION

Is there a theme God has been speaking to me about this week through Bible reading, worship, books, or sermons?

....

....

....

The questions I have for God right now are:

....

....

....

NEXT WEEK

What am I looking forward to?

....

Next week's memory verse:

....

Week of:

....

Then Jesus said to the Jews who had believed him, "If you continue in my word, you really are my disciples. You will know the truth, and the truth will set you free."

John 8:31-32

Date:

Today, I feel ....

READ

Today, I read ....

What stood out to me is:

....

....

REFLECT

What I best sense God speaking to me is:

....

....

....

The one thing I will surrender to God today is:

....

....

....

One next step I can take today is:

....

....

RESPOND

REMEMBER

Date: ....

Today, I feel ....

READ

Today, I read ....

What stood out to me is:

....

....

REFLECT

What I best sense God speaking to me is:

....

....

....

The one thing I will surrender to God today is:

....

....

....

One next step I can take today is:

....

....

RESPOND

REMEMBER

Date: ....

Today, I feel ....

READ

Today, I read ....

What stood out to me is:

....

....

REFLECT

What I best sense God speaking to me is:

....

....

....

The one thing I will surrender to God today is:

....

....

....

One next step I can take today is:

....

....

RESPOND

REMEMBER

Date:

Today, I feel ....

READ

Today, I read ....

What stood out to me is:

....

....

REFLECT

What I best sense God speaking to me is:

....

....

....

The one thing I will surrender to God today is:

....

....

....

One next step I can take today is:

....

....

RESPOND

REMEMBER

Date:

Today, I feel ....

READ

Today, I read ....

What stood out to me is:

....

....

REFLECT

What I best sense God speaking to me is:

....

....

....

The one thing I will surrender to God today is:

....

....

....

One next step I can take today is:

....

....

RESPOND

REMEMBER

Weekly Reflection

PERSONAL REFLECTION

What went well this week?

....

....

Three things I am grateful for are:

1. ....

2. ....

3. ....

What feeling(s) did I experience most frequently? Why?

....

....

....

What thoughts or worries have come to mind most frequently?

....

....

RELATIONAL REFLECTION

Who do I need to forgive?

....

With whom do I need to make things right?

....

I will do that by:

....

....

One person I will connect with next week is:

....

SPIRITUAL REFLECTION

Is there a theme God has been speaking to me about this week through Bible reading, worship, books, or sermons?

....

....

....

The questions I have for God right now are:

....

....

....

NEXT WEEK

What am I looking forward to?

....

Next week's memory verse:

....

Week of:

....

Do not be conformed to this age, but be transformed by the renewing of your mind, so that you may discern what is the good, pleasing, and perfect will of God.

Romans 12:2

Date:

Today, I feel ....

READ

Today, I read ....

What stood out to me is:

....

....

REFLECT

What I best sense God speaking to me is:

....

....

....

The one thing I will surrender to God today is:

....

....

....

One next step I can take today is:

....

....

RESPOND

REMEMBER

Date:

Today, I feel ....

READ

Today, I read ....

What stood out to me is:

....

....

REFLECT

What I best sense God speaking to me is:

....

....

....

The one thing I will surrender to God today is:

....

....

....

One next step I can take today is:

....

....

RESPOND

REMEMBER

Date: ....

Today, I feel ....

READ

Today, I read ....

What stood out to me is:

....

....

REFLECT

What I best sense God speaking to me is:

....

....

....

The one thing I will surrender to God today is:

....

....

....

One next step I can take today is:

....

....

RESPOND

REMEMBER

Date:

Today, I feel ....

READ

Today, I read ....

What stood out to me is:

....

....

REFLECT

What I best sense God speaking to me is:

....

....

....

The one thing I will surrender to God today is:

....

....

....

One next step I can take today is:

....

....

RESPOND

REMEMBER

Date:
....

Today, I feel ....

READ

Today, I read ....

What stood out to me is:

....

....

REFLECT

What I best sense God speaking to me is:

....

....

....

The one thing I will surrender to God today is:

....

....

....

One next step I can take today is:

....

....

RESPOND

REMEMBER

Weekly Reflection

PERSONAL REFLECTION

What went well this week?

....

....

Three things I am grateful for are:

1. ....

2. ....

3. ....

What feeling(s) did I experience most frequently? Why?

....

....

....

What thoughts or worries have come to mind most frequently?

....

....

RELATIONAL REFLECTION

Who do I need to forgive?

....

With whom do I need to make things right?

....

I will do that by:

....

....

One person I will connect with next week is:

....

SPIRITUAL REFLECTION

Is there a theme God has been speaking to me about this week through Bible reading, worship, books, or sermons?

....

....

....

The questions I have for God right now are:

....

....

....

NEXT WEEK

What am I looking forward to?

....

Next week's memory verse:

....

Resources

Emotions

Try to narrow down your emotions and be specifc about how you are feeling.

Choose the initial emotion you feel (happy, fearful, disgusted, sad, angry, bad, surprised) and work towards the column on the far right.[4]

HAPPY	Content	Free Joyful
	Interested	Curious Inquisitive
	Proud	Successful Confident
	Accepted	Respected Valued
	Powerful	Courageous Creative
	Peaceful	Loving Thankful
	Trusting	Sensitive Intimate
	Optimistic	Hopeful Inspired

FEARFUL	Scared	Helpless Frightened
	Anxious	Overwhelmed Worried
	Insecure	Inadequate Inferior
	Weak	Worthless Insignificant
	Rejected	Excluded Persecuted
	Threatened	Nervous Exposed

DISGUSTED	Disapproving	Judgmental Embarrassed
	Disappointed	Appalled Revolted
	Awful	Nauseated Detestable
	Repelled	Horrified Hesitant

SURPRISED	Startled	Shocked Dismayed
	Confused	Disillusioned Perplexed
	Amazed	Astonished Awed
	Excited	Eager Energetic

ANGRY	Let down	Betrayed
		Resentful
	Humiliated	Disrespected
		Ridiculed
	Bitter	Indignant
		Violated
	Mad	Furious
		Jealous
	Aggressive	Provoked
		Hostile
	Frustrated	Infuriated
		Annoyed
	Distant	Withdrawn
		Numb
	Critical	Skeptical
		Dismissive

BAD	Bored	Indifferent
		Apathetic
	Busy	Pressured
		Rushed
	Stressed	Overwhelmed
		Out of control
	Tired	Sleepy
		Unfocused

SAD	Lonely	Isolated
		Abandoned
	Vulnerable	Victimised
		Fragile
	Despairing	Grieving
		Powerless
	Guilty	Ashamed
		Remorseful
	Depressed	Inferior
		Empty
	Hurt	Embarassed
		Disappointed

Prayer of Forgiveness

God, I choose to forgive [name]. When he/she [words or situation that caused hurt] it made me feel [emotions and pain].

As I have accepted your forgiveness for my own sins and shortcomings, I offer this forgiveness to [name]. Whether or not he/she deserves my forgiveness and whether he/she asks for forgiveness, I will freely give it because of your death on the cross.

When I see [name] again, help me recall this prayer and hold captive any thoughts towards him/her that are not merciful and filled with grace. Help me to see him/her the way you do and help me to love him/her as you do.

I pray that [name] would receive your forgiveness and your blessing. I release him/her to your care and choose to no longer carry this burden of bitterness. Please heal my heart and help me not to allow this hurt to distance myself from others. Thank you for your extravagant love.

Amen.

Prayer of Repentance

God, forgive me for [words or actions]. My words/actions caused
[result of words or actions]. Above all, I know my sin is separating
me from your intimate presence. I am sorry, God.

Please help me release the shame and regret I feel, knowing that I am
undeserving of your extravagant love and endless grace, yet you give
them to me freely. I forgive myself and let go of all self-hatred and
condemnation.

Allow your conviction to continue to bring me towards you in
repentance instead of hiding my sin. Shine your light of truth in any
other area of my heart that I need to repent of now.

[Pause for reflection and repeat the first paragraph for any other
areas of sin God brings to mind.]

Thank you for your forgiveness. Help me resist the temptation
to repeat my sin or punish myself for my past sins. I accept your
forgiveness and move forward in love and grace.

Amen.

Making Amends

WHAT DOES IT MEAN TO MAKE AMENDS?

Making amends means to do something to correct a mistake that one has made or a bad situation that one has caused.[5]

It involves 3 parts:
- Sincere apology
- Change of behavior
- Restitution

APOLOGY

Your apology should be made in person or in writing. It should be specific about what you did that hurt them and the consequences that resulted. This is not a time to discuss what the other person may have done to hurt you—you are taking responsibility for your own actions, not pointing fingers or passing blame. Additionally, it is not your responsibility to encourage their forgiveness, nor is it your right to receive their forgiveness, so do not ask the other person to forgive you.

CHANGE OF BEHAVIOR

An apology without a change in behavior is worthless. Your actions speak louder than your words. True repentance is displayed when we turn away from our sin and act in the opposite spirit.

RESTITUTION

Beyond an apology and change of behavior, restitution needs to be made. This may mean returning what you stole, fixing what you broke, or paying for something to be replaced. This may be easier to see how it applies to tangible objects, but the same applies for people. It's much more difficult to heal a person than to fix a car, but do what you can to make up for the damage you caused.

DIRECT AND INDIRECT AMENDS

From the *12 Steps of Freedom Session*[6]: "We made specific and direct amends to those we have hurt whenever possible, except when to do so would further injure them or others who are innocent. For such persons, we made specific and indirect amends."

There are times when it is unwise or impossible to make a direct amends to the person you hurt.

An indirect amends should be made if a direct amends would cause serious, additional harm to the person you hurt. If you're considering an indirect amends, ask yourself: "Am I avoiding this conversation to protect myself or him/her?" This is also a good time to find someone you trust to confess this situation and ask for an objective opinion on whether you should directly or indirectly make amends.

If the person you hurt is no longer alive or they are unreachable, you should still make amends indirectly. Consider writing a letter of apology and discarding it and/or make a donation or serve an organization that would honor the person.

Galatians

Galatians 1:1-10

Galatians 1:11-24

Galatians 2:1-10

Galatians 2:11-21

Galatians 3:1-14

Galatians 3:15-22

Galatians 3:23-4:7

Galatians 4:8-20

Galatians 4:21-31

Galatians 5:1-12

Galatians 5:13-26

Galatians 6

James

James 1:1-8

James 1:9-11

James 1:12-18

James 1:19-21

James 1:22-27

James 2:1-7

James 2:8-13

James 2:14-19

James 2:20-26

James 3:1-6

James 3:7-12

James 3:13-16

James 3:17-18

James 4:1-6

James 4:7-10

James 4:11-12

James 3:13-17

James 5:1-6

James 5:7-12

James 5:13-16

James 5:17-20

1 Peter   2 Peter

Additional Resources

For additional resources, including more Bible reading
plans, visit www.tarynnergaard.com/resources.

Notes

1   Freeman, Emily P. "04: Record What You Learn." *Emily P. Freeman*, https://emilypfreeman.com/podcast/the-next-right-thing/04-record-learn. Accessed 6 January 2020

2   Smietana, Bob. "LifeWay Research: Americans Are Fond of the Bible, Don't Actually Read It." *LifeWay Research*, LifeWay Research, 25 April 2017, https://lifewayresearch. com/2017/04/25/lifeway-research-americans-are-fond-of-the-Bible-dont-actually-read-it. Accessed 7 January 2020.

3   I will be forever grateful to Ken Dyck, creator of Freedom Session, for his teaching on Bible reading.

4   These emotions were orginally published as an emotion wheel.

    Schuster, Sarah. "The 'Emotion Chart' My Therapist Gave Me That I Didn't Know I Needed." *Yahoo!Lifestyle*, Yahoo.com, 28 November 2018, https://www.yahoo.com/lifestyle/apos-emotion-chart-apos-therapist-002028240.html. Accessed 7 January 2020.

5   "Make amends." *The Merriam-Webster.com Dictionary*, Merriam-Webster Inc., https://www.merriam-webster.com/dictionary/make%20amends. Accessed 6 January 2020.

6   Dyck, Ken. "12 Steps of Freedom Session." *Freedom Session*, Freedom Session International, https://freedomsession.com/12-steps-of-freedom-session. Accessed 6 January 2020.

About the Author

Taryn Nergaard is a writer, podcaster, and graphic designer. Her interests and vocation are diverse but rooted in the same calling: to tell the truth beautifully.

Taryn lives in the stunning Fraser Valley of British Columbia, Canada with her husband and four kids. When she's not busy homeschooling or running her design & marketing company, you'll find her enjoying a cup of coffee and a good book, or curled up on the couch binge watching her current favorite show.

Made in the USA
Middletown, DE
18 January 2020